G000036713

The official Barbie Annual 2003

Written by Jane Clempner
Designed by Sheryl Bone

Published in Great Britain in 2002 by
Egmont Books Limited,
239 Kensington High Street
London, W8 6SA.
Printed in Italy

ISBN: 0 7498 5606 8

This is my Barbie Annual 2003

Name:

vicky may orme

I am ....*9*.... years and ....
months old.

My hair is ....

My eyes are ....*ster blue*.........

My favourite colour is .....*gold*.....

My best friend is .....*Tega Amy*.....

I love to wear .....*ali*......................

I love to play ....

I love…Barbie!

CONTENTS

Barbie™

Ready, set ...go girls!

Welcome to your very special, very own Barbie Annual!

This year it's action-packed and full of the things you love —
stories, puzzles, colouring, fashion and some cool ideas for
things to make and do.

Are you ready for some serious girl-type fun?

Then let's go ... Barbie

"Welcome to the team!"

Choose colours to make us the smartest girls in town!

Get set for...
FUN!
Barbie

Then join us by drawing a picture, or sticking a photo of yourself here!

"B is for Barbie and B is for Basketball!"

Basketball is my favourite sport and a great way to keep fit, hang out with friends, and have fun all at once!

Circle the things you see here that start with the letter B.

Now it's your turn!

Write your name here ....

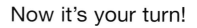

How many things can your draw that start with the same letter as your name?

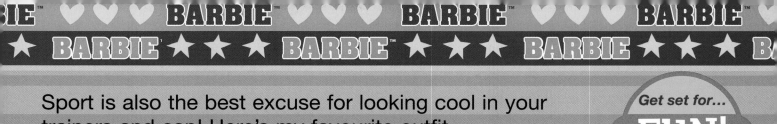

Sport is also the best excuse for looking cool in your trainers and cap! Here's my favourite outfit.

Can you colour it in and then design one for yourself?

BARBIE'S B-TEAM

"Barbie style is all about girls who want to join in and have fun!"

"B – A – R... B – I - E! Go Barbie! Go Barbie!"
The crowd chanted and cheered, but Barbie's team still didn't score!

"We're breaking all records..." said Sophie, as the B-team made their way to the showers, "for being the worst basketball team in school history!"

"It's better to play and lose, than not to play at all!" said Barbie, encouragingly.
"Aye, aye captain!" laughed Rachel. "I'm only here for the refreshments anyway!"
"And for our cool T-shirts!" said Kirsten, doing a twirl.

On the front was a bright, pink, letter B, and on the back each player had their own message: ... is for Barbie's Team! ... is for Beautiful! Or ... Better go back to bed!

The girls had more fun making up new captions than training. Perhaps that's why they never won!

Barbie™

Just then, Angel Morgan put her head around the changing room door. She was captain of the A-team, leaders of the school league. They had the smartest team-strip and the loudest cheerleaders! Angel's father just happened to be Head of Sports and liked to make sure his daughter's team won.

"If you want my advice," said Angel, (Angel by name, but not by nature!) "you need to get fit! We train three times a week and at weekends. And ditch those daft T-shirts. If you looked like a real team, you'd play like a real team!"

"She's unbearable!" said Becky, when Angel had gone.
"Yes, but, she does have a point," added Rachel. "We are the only team in school not to have won a single match! I know what I'm going to put on my next T-shirt. B is for... Bottom of the league!"
"Don't talk like that!" said Barbie. "Someone has to come last – so we're doing everyone else a favour!"

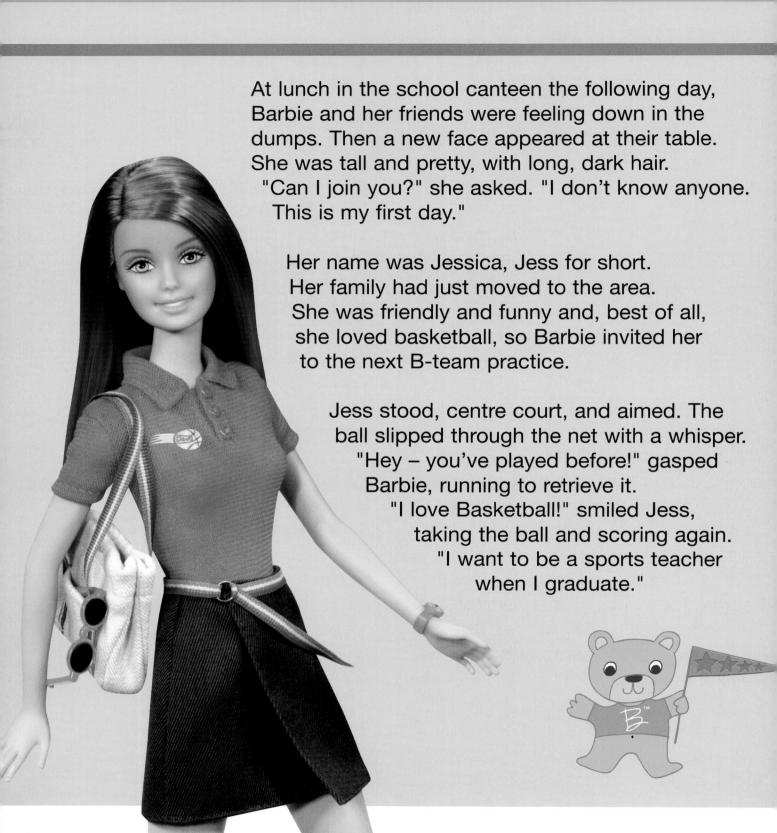

At lunch in the school canteen the following day,
Barbie and her friends were feeling down in the
dumps. Then a new face appeared at their table.
She was tall and pretty, with long, dark hair.
"Can I join you?" she asked. "I don't know anyone.
This is my first day."

Her name was Jessica, Jess for short.
Her family had just moved to the area.
She was friendly and funny and, best of all,
she loved basketball, so Barbie invited her
to the next B-team practice.

Jess stood, centre court, and aimed. The
ball slipped through the net with a whisper.
"Hey – you've played before!" gasped
Barbie, running to retrieve it.
"I love Basketball!" smiled Jess,
taking the ball and scoring again.
"I want to be a sports teacher
when I graduate."

That was a turning point in the history of the B-team! The following Saturday they won their first match! Jess worked out a strict training plan. And, as their skills improved so did their scores! Barbie was delighted. As the weeks slipped by her team began to creep up the league!

Angel Morgan began to look worried!

"She can't believe her eyes!" giggled Bethany, when Angel came along to watch them train. Barbie noticed she was watching Jess most closely of all. That evening Angel gave Jess a lift home. Then she started giving her a lift to school in the mornings. Soon they were sitting together at lunch, and in lessons. Angel liked to win. And now she was winning Jess over to her side.

Meanwhile, the B-team had been playing so well and putting in so much effort that they had crept up the league and were now lying in joint top position with the A's! With only one match left to play, next Saturday's final would decide the League Championship!

On the final practice night, Barbie's team were warming up in the sports hall. Jess arrived late.
"Hi Barbie," she said. "I'm really sorry but I can't stay tonight I… I have too much homework. See you…" And with that she ran off. Barbie knew where she was going.

Barbie arrived at school half an hour early the next
morning and waited in the cloakroom.
"I thought we were friends," she said, when Jess came
in to hang up her coat. "Why have you joined the A's?"
Jess blushed and looked down. Then shook her hair
back from her face and looked at Barbie. "I had no
choice, Barbie. I need Angel's dad to give me a good
report if I'm going to get into Sports College next year. My parents say I
must take sport seriously. I'm really sorry." Barbie walked away, sadly.
"We can still be friends though, can't we?" said Jess, coming after her.
Barbie turned and managed to smile.
"Of course we can. Hey - it's only a game, right!"

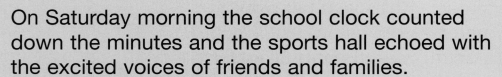

On Saturday morning the school clock counted
down the minutes and the sports hall echoed with
the excited voices of friends and families.

But the B-team changing room was strangely
quiet.
"Come on, cheer up!" said captain Barbie,
clapping her hands together. "This is a dream
come true! Who would ever have believed we
would be playing the A's in the league final!"
"Yes, but our best player is on the opposition!"
grumbled Kirsten.
"I know," said Barbie. "We *can* do it without her.
Come on. Look at my new T-shirt!"
It said: B... is for Believing we're the Best!

The cheer that greeted them as they stepped out onto court drowned out the A-team cheerleaders! Then, the crowd fell silent and the referee put the whistle to his lips. He was about to blow when Angel ran over and stopped him. "Hold on – I'm one player short!"

At that moment, a door banged and in ran Jess. Everyone turned and stared. She wasn't wearing the smart A-team strip, but a bright pink T-shirt! She ran onto the court and gave a twirl. It said: B is for … Best friends sticking together!

Jess took up her position next to Barbie, and Angel had to bring on a sub.

Then the whistle blew. 50 minutes later, the whistle blew again and everyone cheered. With the final score standing at 25 – 25, for the first time in school history, the League Cup would be shared!

Which meant that everyone shook hands and agreed to join together for a fabulous party to celebrate.

All except Angel, who stormed off in a huff!

That was one of the happiest days of Barbie's life!

Barbie™

Team Talk!

I've been asked to design an emblem for our team.
Here are some of my ideas. Can you find two the same?

Now can you help by designing
an emblem for me?

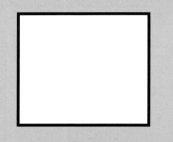

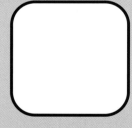

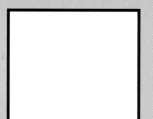

I love all kinds of sports —
some I like to play and some I like to watch!
Can you match these things into pairs and name each sport?

Replace the numbers with letters from the alphabet to
discover Barbie's secret message to her team!

20.18.25.   25.15.21.18.   2.5.19.20

_ _ _   _ _ _ _   _ _ _ _

Go Barbie!
Go Barbie!

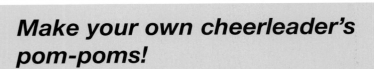

BARBIE™

Make your own cheerleader's pom-poms!

You need:

Three sheets of crepe paper– in your team colours
Scissors
Pencil or pen
Sticky tape
Ribbon

1

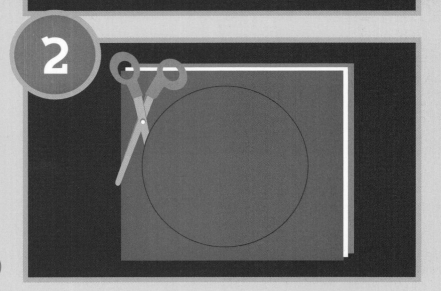

Here's how:

Put your sheets of crepe paper on top of each other.

2

Draw and then cut out a large circle (about 40 – 50 cm wide) making sure you cut through each sheet. You may need to ask a grown-up to help you.

3

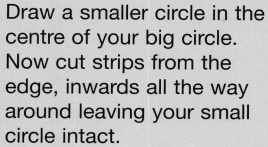

Draw a smaller circle in the centre of your big circle. Now cut strips from the edge, inwards all the way around leaving your small circle intact.

Scrunch up the centre circle and hold in place with sticky tape. This is the handle of your pom-pom.

4

Repeat from the beginning to make your second pom-pom.

Tie ribbon around your handles. Leave a loop to wear around your wrist.

5

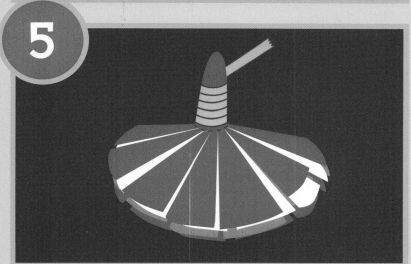

Now... Go! Go! Go! Make pom-poms for your friends and cheer on your favourite team! Why not make up your own cheerleaders' rhyme and some nifty dance steps too!

It's Competition Time!

We've got 22 super Barbie prizes to give away, courtesy of Worlds Apart Ltd:

First Prize:
Barbie Ready Bed

The inflatable sleeping bag that's perfect for sleepovers! Snuggle up! Bedtime can be lots of fun. This super-soft and comfy bed comes with a free carry case and pump. Sweet Dreams...Zzzz!

Second Prize:
Barbie Pop Tidy

The portable storage bin for all your Barbie toys and accessories. The Pop tidy "pops" up and down in seconds and can be used indoors or out. Keeps all your special things tidy and safe!

5 Third Prizes:
Barbie Pocket Kite

The full-sized kite that folds down and fits in your pocket! It's ready to fly and needs no assembly. Fun on the go!

15 Runners-up Prizes:
Barbie Fashion Tent

The funky, heart-shaped tent with its own fold-out catwalk! Stage your very own fashion show and let Barbie show off her latest looks! Stylish fun for Barbie and you!

How to enter:

All you have to do is to answer this question:

What is Barbie's favourite colour?

Write your answer, and your name, address and age, on a postcard or the back of a sealed envelope, then post it to this address:

Barbie Annual Competition,
Egmont Books,
Unit 7, Millbank House,
Riverside Park,
Bollin Walk,Wilmslow,
Cheshire SK9 1BJ

Entries must reach us by 24 January 2003.

Rules
1) The winners will be chosen at random and notified by post. 2) The judges' decision will be final. No correspondence will be entered into. 3) The winners' names will be made available from Egmont Books (on request) after 3 February 2003. Please enclose a stamped addressed envelope. 4) Employees (and their relatives) of Egmont Books and associated companies are not eligible to enter. 5) Entries are limited to one per person. 6) The competition is open to non-residents of the UK, Channel Islands and Ireland. 7) The publishers reserve the right to vary prizes, subject to availability. 8) The closing date for entries is 24 January 2003.

Now choose colours for
Barbie's latest look.

Choose your favourite
colours for Barbie.

Art attack

"I just love to paint, draw and create!"

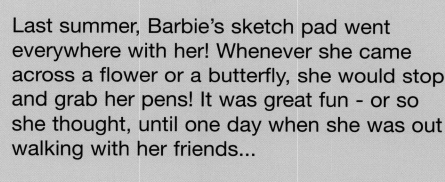

Last summer, Barbie's sketch pad went everywhere with her! Whenever she came across a flower or a butterfly, she would stop and grab her pens! It was great fun - or so she thought, until one day when she was out walking with her friends...

"So, what do you think of my new bike, Barbie?" asked Christie. "It was my birthday present."
"I'm not into bikes right now, " said Barbie, "because I can't draw them!"
They walked on silently for a few minutes.

"Diggory, my so-called male hamster, has just had six babies!" announced Teresa.
"Aw, how cute," breathed Christie. "Can I come over and see them later?"
"Sure! Why don't you come too Barbie?"

"Not tonight, I'm busy. I have to work on my sketches. I'm hoping to get some published in the school magazine. Oh wow! Look over there. I must draw that tree. The colour, the shape. It's perfect."

Barbie ran over, sat in front of the tree, pulled out her pad and began to draw. Christie and Teresa were left stranded.
"Not now, Barbie!" called Teresa. "We want an ice-cream. Let's go."
"Bring me a lolly," shouted Barbie.
"I must just draw this before the light changes."

The others exchanged a look and set off towards the ice cream van, whispering. They spent longer than was really necessary choosing.

"Here you are. One lolly for the artist," said Christie.
"Wow, Barbie, your sketch is really good!" said Teresa, over-enthusiastically.
"Oh yes," agreed Christie. "You should hold an exhibition or something!"

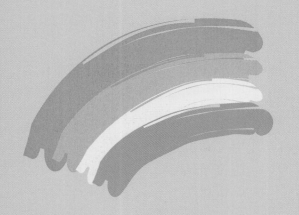

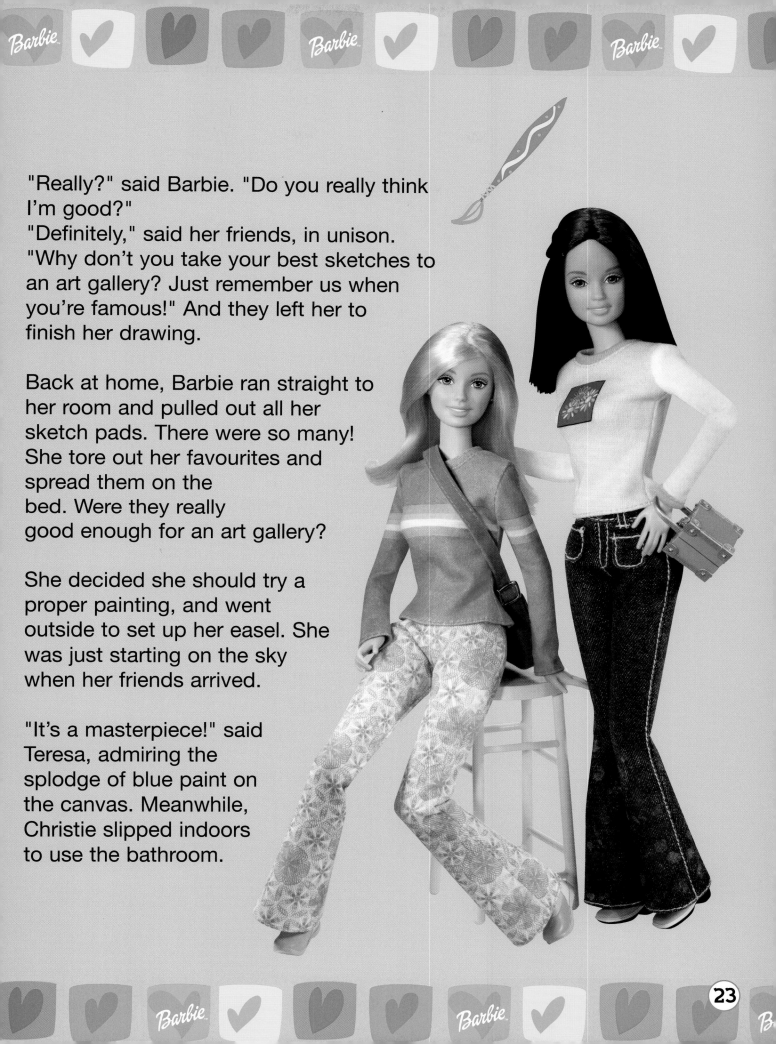

"Really?" said Barbie. "Do you really think I'm good?"

"Definitely," said her friends, in unison. "Why don't you take your best sketches to an art gallery? Just remember us when you're famous!" And they left her to finish her drawing.

Back at home, Barbie ran straight to her room and pulled out all her sketch pads. There were so many! She tore out her favourites and spread them on the bed. Were they really good enough for an art gallery?

She decided she should try a proper painting, and went outside to set up her easel. She was just starting on the sky when her friends arrived.

"It's a masterpiece!" said Teresa, admiring the splodge of blue paint on the canvas. Meanwhile, Christie slipped indoors to use the bathroom.

"What's she doing in there?" said Barbie, when several minutes had passed.
"Here she is!" said Teresa, running to join Christie and ushering her through the garden gate. "Um.. we have to go now, Barbie. Bring your painting round later... bye!"
"Strange!" said Barbie, returning to her work.

Ten minutes later, she threw her paintbrush on the floor. "It's hopeless! This paint's too runny! I'm better at sketching." And she went inside to gather up her sketches.
"I'll take them round to Teresa's and she can help me choose the best ones," she said.

But when she stepped into her bedroom she let out a scream. "Aaaargh! I've been burgled!"

She raced to Teresa's house. The front door was open and Barbie ran through and into the garden where Teresa and Christie were cuddling six little bundles of tawny fur. They both looked up.
"Hi Barbie – what's wrong?"

"I've… I've been burgled! You were right. My work must be valuable. Someone's stolen all my sketches! What am I going to do? We have to go to the Police. We have to… we… what… what are you two laughing at?"

Her friends could stifle their giggles no longer.

"Yes," admitted Teresa. "You were burgled. And here is your thief!" She pointed to Diggory, her hamster, curled up in a bed made of lovely shredded sketch paper!

"I… I…" stammered Barbie. "My sketches! Oh… OK… I get it. Maybe you're right!" And she started to laugh.

"You were being SO boring," said Christie. "Your 'art' was all you could talk about!"

"And you didn't have any time for us. We're your best friends!" added Teresa.

"I'm sorry," said Barbie. "Here, can I hold one of the babies? And hey, tomorrow let's go on a bike ride – and I promise – I'll leave my sketch pad at home!"

Sometimes even Barbie needs a reality check!

25

Quick on the draw!

Here are some of my favourite sketch patterns - the ones Diggory didn't chew! Will you finish them for me?

Here are some more of my sketches and doodles.
Can you match them into pairs?

HBSRU

`- - - - -`

REAPP

`- - - - -`

LEASE

`- - - - -`

TRAWE

`- - - - -`

LINCEP

`- - - - - -`

NAPTI

`- - - - -`

Unscramble these words to find six tools an artist might need.

There are lots of words that describe colour.

Can you match these colours to their describing word?
I've joined 'red' with 'ruby' to show you how its done!

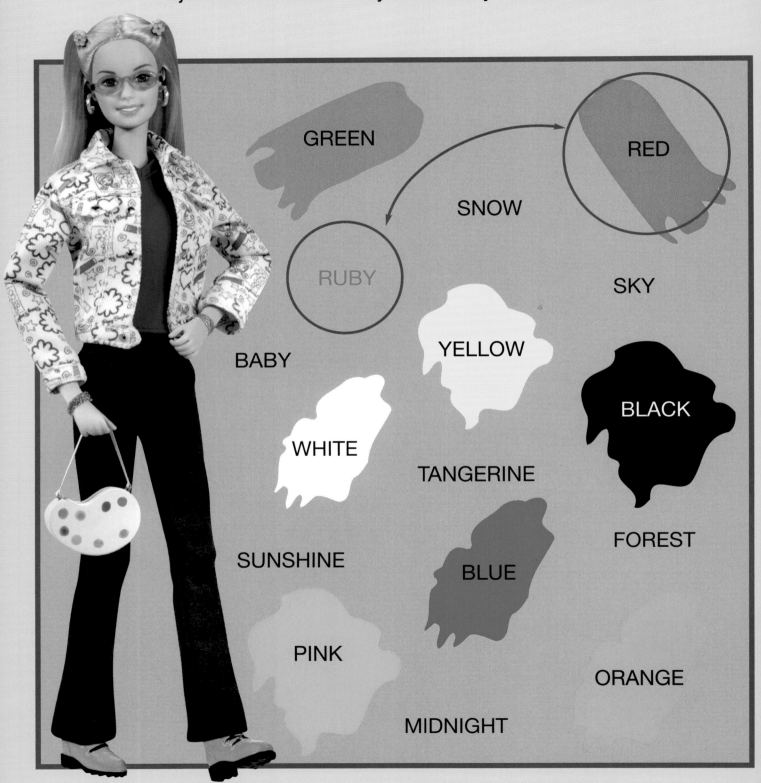

GREEN

RED

SNOW

RUBY

SKY

BABY

YELLOW

WHITE

BLACK

TANGERINE

SUNSHINE

FOREST

BLUE

PINK

ORANGE

MIDNIGHT

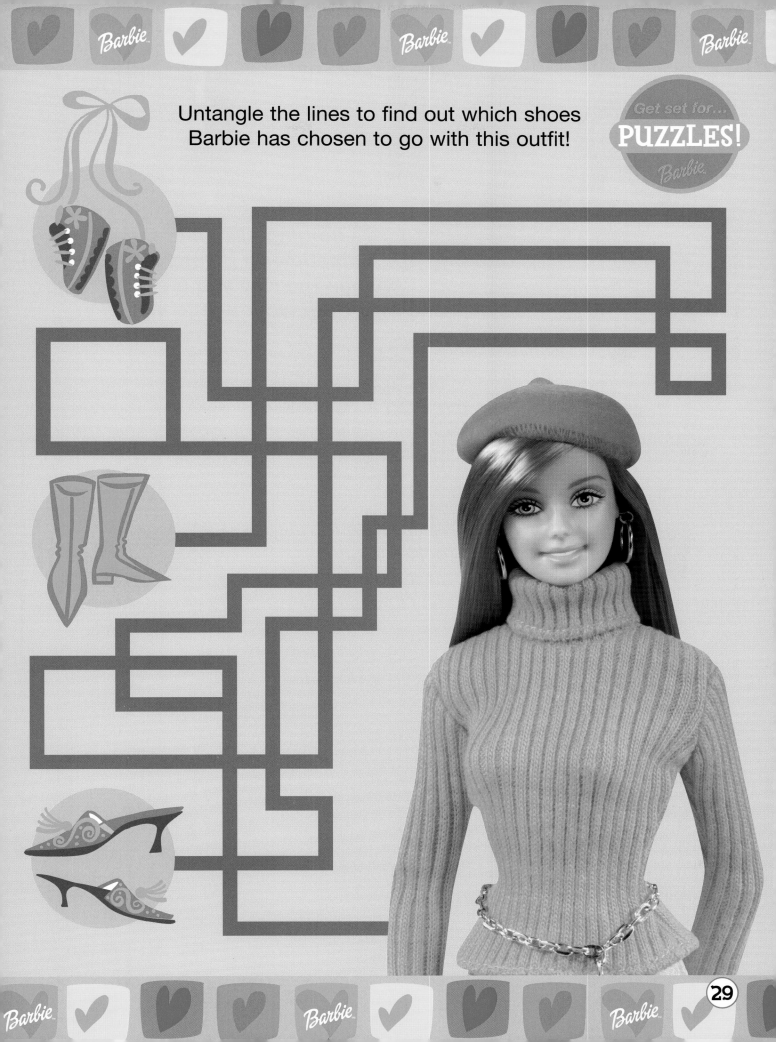

Untangle the lines to find out which shoes Barbie has chosen to go with this outfit!

The Fairytale Ball

"There's nothing I like more than dressing up! Sometimes a glamorous gown can change the way you feel... and may even work a little magic!"

It was to be the most talked-about party of the year. A Fairytale Ball held in a fabulous mansion. Even the invitation was spectacular - glittering letters printed on gold card. It read:

You are invited to:
The Fairytale Masked Ball
Stockley Manor
21st June
Fancy Dress Only

All proceeds to Hayton Children's Hospital

I phoned Ken straight away.
"Of course I'm going!" he said. "Would I miss the chance to dance with the most beautiful girl I know?"
"What shall we go as?" I asked.
"Hmm... How about Cinderella and Prince Charming? We'll make a stunning couple!"

I was so excited! A card had dropped through my letterbox that very day with details of a new dress-hire shop. So I dialed the number.

"I've been expecting you," said a man's voice. "Come along this afternoon at three."

I met Ken in the busy street outside the shop. The sign above the door said:

"Seeing is not believing"

"Funny name for a fancy dress shop!" said Ken. "And it looks tiny." But when we stepped inside the walls seemed to expand around us into an ocean of colour. Amazing costumes in silk, velvet, taffeta and fur were draped from ceiling to floor. The shelves were stacked with necklaces, tiaras and gloves. Sequins and beads sparkled in the light. Wigs, hats and shoes spilled from boxes. It was every girl's wildest dressing-up dream!

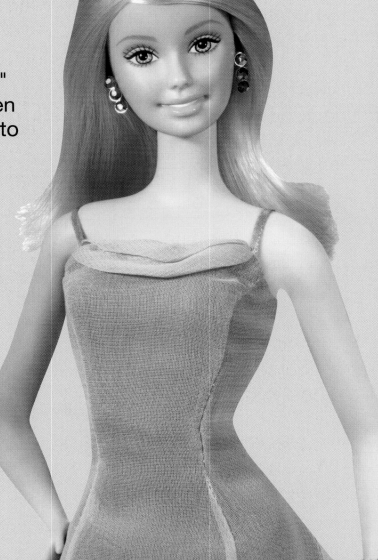

Suddenly, from between two gowns, appeared an old man with a whiff of white hair. He was carrying something gorgeous in pink taffeta. "This is what you are looking for!" he said, handing me a dress, satin slippers and sequined mask. "You will look perfect! And, for Sir," he turned to Ken, "a matching suit with pink lapels to make you as charming as a Prince!"

"Weird!" said Ken, as we stepped back out into the sunlight clutching our outfits. "Was he a mind-reader?!"

Despite the warm sun I felt a shiver run down my spine. The whole experience had been slightly odd.

But when I thought of my beautiful pink gown I felt happy and excited again and couldn't wait for Saturday to come.
Have you ever felt like a Princess? Well I did that night. The gown was perfect. The slippers made me want to dance. I stood in front of the mirror and held the glittering mask to my face. I was ready to make a grand entrance...

I stepped out of the taxi onto the gravel drive and looked up. Stockley Manor was dazzling against a starry sky. At the top of the steps I handed my ticket to a smart doorman and glanced at the photo of Hayton Hospital. It made me feel good to know that I was helping sick children without having to try too hard!

Then I heard the band begin to play and wafted my way through the huge doorway leading to the ballroom. I looked down from the top of the staircase. It was just as I imagined. The chandelier, the music, the masked couples. I glanced at my watch. Ken should be arriving very soon, then we would start the dancing. But, as I looked, I realised there was a couple already on the dance floor! All eyes were on a handsome man in a suit with pink lapels and a graceful girl... wearing a ball gown **identical to mine!**

I held onto the banister to steady myself. I looked again, hoping I was mistaken. This was every girl's worst nightmare! But no. We were identical, right down to the pink satin slippers! That old man in the shop! How many other girls had he hired the 'perfect' dress to? I looked around nervously. The couple moved my way. She was delicate and probably beautiful - I couldn't really see. Then the man's mask slipped. It couldn't be? Surely not! **It was... Ken!**

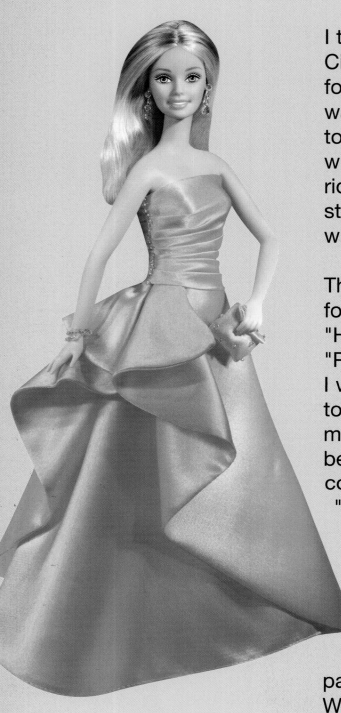

I turned and fled, not feeling one bit like Cinderella! I pushed past people and found a side door that led out into the walled gardens where I stopped and tried to catch my breath. What was he doing with her?! I felt humiliated, angry and ridiculous all at once. I sat on a cold, stone seat and allowed my eyes to fill with warm tears.

Then I heard footsteps behind me.
"Here!" She handed me a tissue.
"Please don't cry!"
I wiped my eyes and she sat down next to me. There we were, side by side, two matching pink Cinderellas! "I've never been to a masked ball before," she continued, handing me another tissue. "Don't be sad. I want tonight to be special for everyone. The hospital said it was OK for me to come, as long as I don't overdo it. I'm hoping to have an operation soon so that I can go dancing more often! I'm going to accept the cheque on behalf of the patients later. Isn't this dress amazing? We both have such good taste! And I've found the most handsome man who just happens to have a matching suit. It's incredible! If it wasn't happening I'd think it was a dream!"

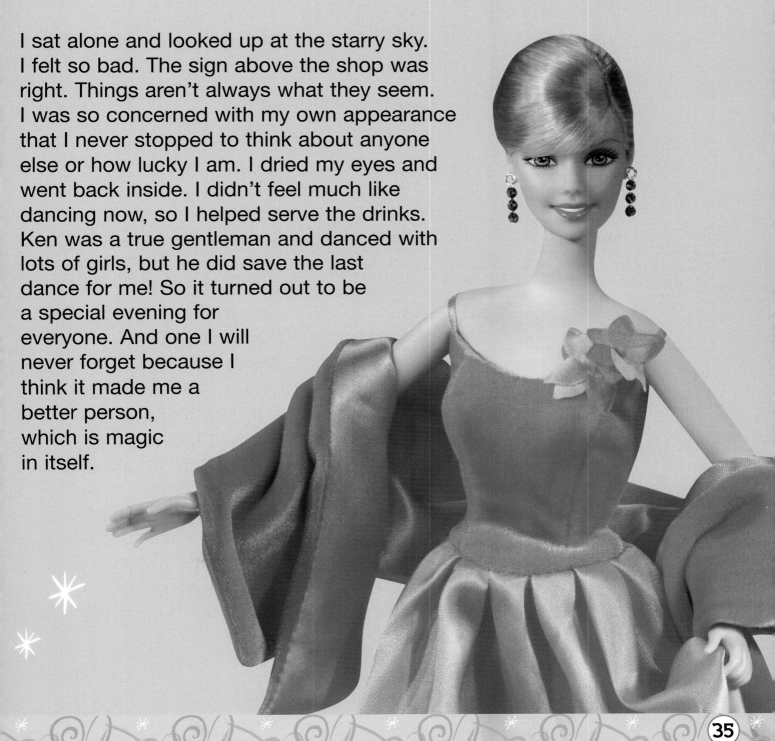

I blinked back my tears and gulped rather loudly. "I...I'm fine now," I fibbed. "I just had something in my eye. Thanks for the tissue. Don't stay out here in the cold. It's your special evening - go back and make the most of it!"

I sat alone and looked up at the starry sky. I felt so bad. The sign above the shop was right. Things aren't always what they seem. I was so concerned with my own appearance that I never stopped to think about anyone else or how lucky I am. I dried my eyes and went back inside. I didn't feel much like dancing now, so I helped serve the drinks. Ken was a true gentleman and danced with lots of girls, but he did save the last dance for me! So it turned out to be a special evening for everyone. And one I will never forget because I think it made me a better person, which is magic in itself.

Which Dressing-up Character suits you?

Go with the flow and find out.

Read the questions and answer – honestly!
If you answer yes follow the blue arrow. If you answer no, follow the red arrow.

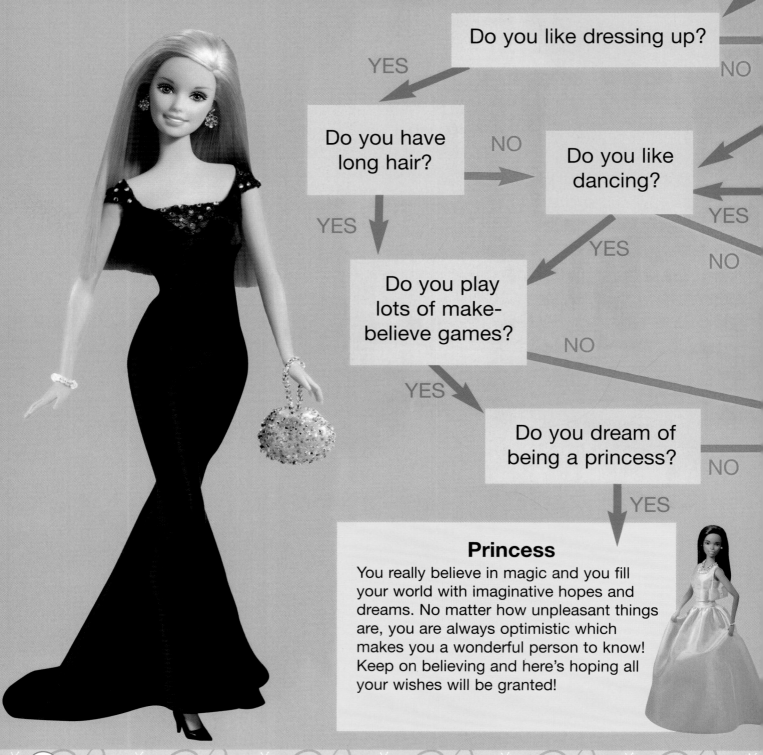

Do you like dressing up?

YES   NO

Do you have long hair?

NO → **Do you like dancing?**

YES   YES   NO

YES ↓

Do you play lots of make-believe games?

NO

YES ↓

Do you dream of being a princess?

NO

YES ↓

Princess

You really believe in magic and you fill your world with imaginative hopes and dreams. No matter how unpleasant things are, you are always optimistic which makes you a wonderful person to know! Keep on believing and here's hoping all your wishes will be granted!

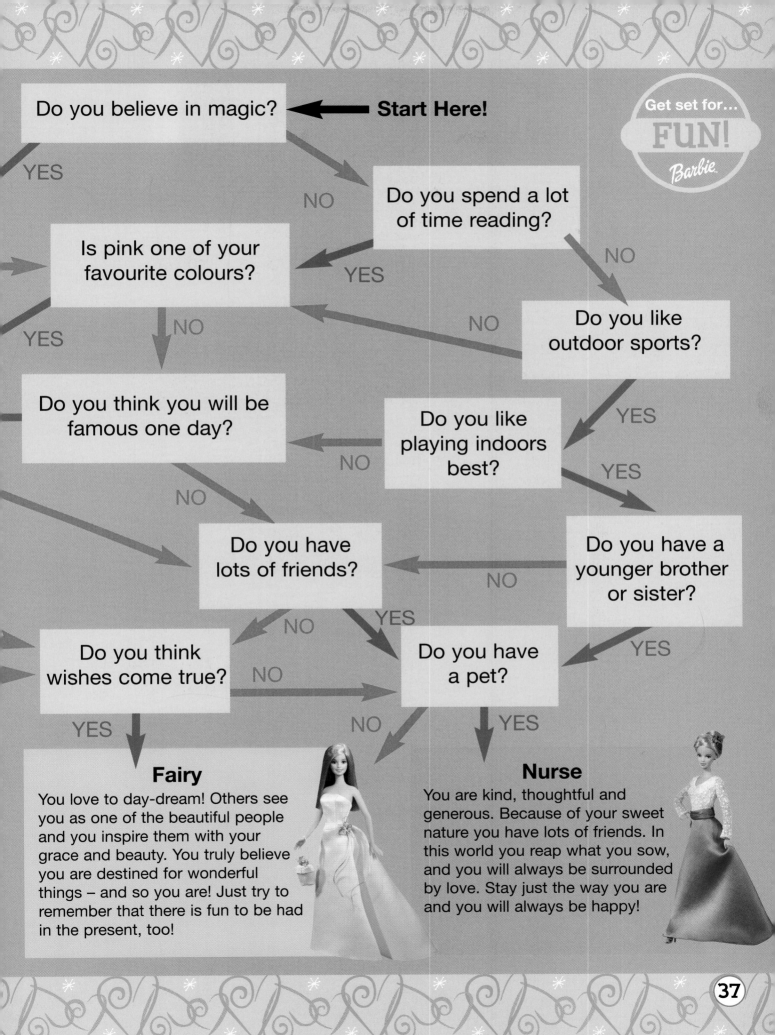

Do you believe in magic? ← **Start Here!**

YES

NO

Get set for...
FUN!
Barbie

Do you spend a lot of time reading?

Is pink one of your favourite colours?

NO

YES

NO

Do you like outdoor sports?

YES

NO

NO

Do you think you will be famous one day?

Do you like playing indoors best?

YES

NO

YES

YES

NO

Do you have lots of friends?

Do you have a younger brother or sister?

NO

NO

YES

YES

Do you think wishes come true?

NO

Do you have a pet?

NO

YES

YES

NO

YES

Fairy

You love to day-dream! Others see you as one of the beautiful people and you inspire them with your grace and beauty. You truly believe you are destined for wonderful things – and so you are! Just try to remember that there is fun to be had in the present, too!

Nurse

You are kind, thoughtful and generous. Because of your sweet nature you have lots of friends. In this world you reap what you sow, and you will always be surrounded by love. Stay just the way you are and you will always be happy!

You too shall go to the Masked Ball!

Make your own fairytale mask.

Perfectly Glamorous ™ Perfectly Glamorous ™

You need:

Tracing paper or a photocopier
Stiff card
Scissors
Sticky tape or glue
Paints or coloured paper
Sequins, doilies, glitter,
ribbon or tinsel for decoration
Wooden barbeque or garden stick

Here's how:

Trace or photocopy the mask
shape from the book.

Put your tracing or photocopy onto
the piece of card and cut around it.

Paint your mask or cover it with coloured paper.

Decorate with the doily, glitter, sequins and ribbon. Let your imagination guide you!

Decorate the rod with ribbon or tinsel and attach to the back of your mask using glue or sticky tape.

Tea for Three™

Barbie was flicking through the empty pages in her diary.

"There's nothing to look forward to," she complained. "No dates, no nights out, not even a tea party!" That gave her an idea. She turned the page to the following Sunday and wrote in very large letters: MY TEA PARTY!

Now she had something to look forward to and plenty to do! Firstly, the guest list. She found a large sheet of paper and wrote the names of her two best friends at the top. Then she wrote some more names, and crossed them out again.

"She plays football on Sundays. She's on holiday. She has chickenpox. She NEVER turns up!"

Barbie looked at her guest list again. "That's it then. It's tea for three! Just Christie, Teresa and me!"

Barbie designed and made the invitations herself. They took two days to make!

Please come for Tea at three
and party with me,
Best friends we'll be
Love and kisses ... Barbie x

She sealed the envelopes with heart stickers and put them on the mantel piece to dry.

Now for the baking! A whole day passed as she stirred, heated and chopped and, worse of all, washed up! But fabulous smells soon filled the kitchen, and after a small disaster with the icing sugar and one tray of burnt cookies, the banquet was prepared!

By the time Sunday came, Barbie thought it strange that neither Christie nor Teresa had replied to their invitations. But they were her best friends. They wouldn't let her down!

She spent the morning hoovering and polishing. Then she set the table with flowers, teacups, plates of sandwiches, cookies and cakes. She pre-boiled the kettle (several times) and dropped the teabags into the pot. Then she put on her party dress and waited for her guests.

The clock struck three. They were always late! After fifteen minutes, Barbie looked out of the window to see if they were coming. At half-past, she stood outside on the pavement with her arms folded. At a quarter to four she was still all alone.

"So much for my best friends," she sighed. "They didn't even let me know. They must have found something better to do than come to my stupid tea party."

She stood up and was just about to throw the cookies in the bin, when the phone rang. It was Christie.

"Hi Barbie. What are you doing? Teresa and I are *so* bored. Don't you just hate Sundays with nothing to do? You want to come skating?"
"B… but what about my tea party?!" stammered Barbie.
"What tea party?" asked Christie.
"The one I sent you an invitation for..." Barbie glanced over at the mantel piece. There were the two envelopes, still drying!

Barbie laughed and explained what had happened. "Poor Barbie!" said Christie. "If we hurry around now, we might just make it. Let's call it tea for three at four!" And that's just what they did!

Make tea party invitations just like Barbie!

You need:

Tracing paper or a photocopier
Scissors
Thin, coloured card
Felt-tipped pens
Glue
Friends to invite!

Here's how:

1

Trace or photocopy the teapot shape from the opposite page.

2

Glue your tracing or photocopy onto your piece of coloured card and cut around it.

3

Colour the design using felt-tipped pens. Glue on glitter or beads to add extra sparkle.

4

Now fill in the blank spaces with your name and the name of your friend.

Tea Party!

Dear_____

Please come for tea at:

_____

_____

love from_____

Make more invitations if you are inviting more than one friend!
Now turn the page and find out how to make your own cookies!

Bake cookies for your Tea Party!

You need:

Kitchen weighing scales
Large mixing bowl
Rolling pin
Two baking trays
Small, shaped cookie cutter
Wire cooling tray

Ingredients:

225g/8oz self-raising flour
Pinch of salt
150g/5oz butter
100g/4oz caster sugar
Beaten egg
Ready-made icing tubes or
Icing sugar, warm water
and food colouring
Chocolate drops and
silver balls

FLOUR

SUGAR

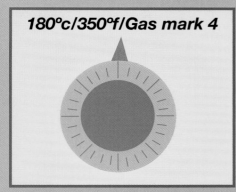

180°c/350°f/Gas mark 4

With a grown-up's help, pre-heat the oven to 180oC/350oF/Gas mark 4 and weigh your ingredients.

Grease two baking trays. Sift the flour and salt into a bowl.

Rub in the butter until the mixture looks like fine breadcrumbs. Add the sugar.

Mix with the beaten egg and knead into a smooth dough. Chill in the fridge for 30 minutes.

Roll out your dough fairly thinly.

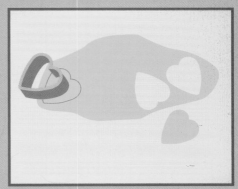

Cut out about 30 cookies and place on the baking trays. Prick well with a fork.

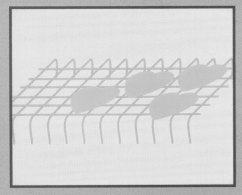

Bake for 10-15 minutes until golden brown. Remove from oven and cool on a wire tray.

Use ready-made icing or make your own by mixing icing sugar with warm water and food colouring.

Decorate with silver balls or chocolate drops. You could make patterns or write the initial of each friend coming for tea.

Can you find ten tea cups hidden in this picture?

There are ten tea-party words hidden
in this wordsearch.

How many can you find?

T	E	A	P	O	T	T	C	A	R	X	N	A
E	O	K	N	S	P	O	O	N	C	N	R	T
A	G	N	C	C	A	K	O	P	L	A	T	E
C	Y	I	T	B	C	A	K	E	S	P	R	I
U	F	F	H	E	Y	S	I	N	V	K	E	N
P	H	E	S	A	U	C	E	R	A	I	F	R
B	E	T	C	S	S	U	G	A	R	N	E	T

TEAPOT   TEACUP   PLATE   SAUCER   KNIFE
COOKIE   CAKE   SPOON   NAPKIN   SUGAR

Barbie's tea party has started but someone is lost!
Can you show her the way to Barbie's house?

Here are some of the things that are magical to me...

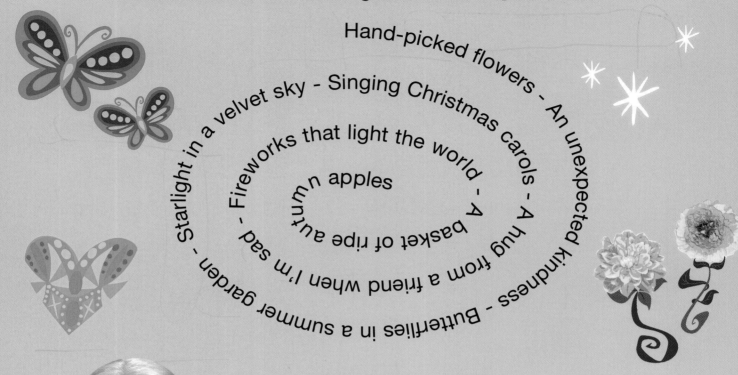

Hand-picked flowers - An unexpected kindness - Butterflies in a summer garden - Starlight in a velvet sky - Singing Christmas carols - A hug from a friend when I'm sad - A basket of ripe autumn apples - Fireworks that light the world

Words are magical too! Can you match these words together to make new words?

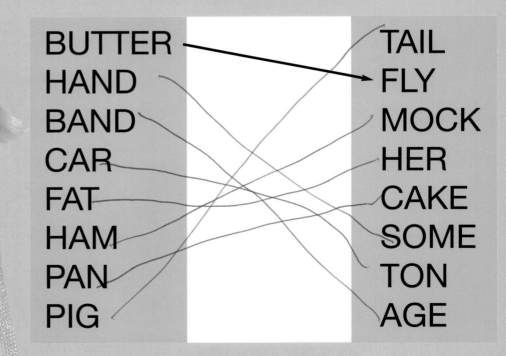

BUTTER	TAIL
HAND	FLY
BAND	MOCK
CAR	HER
FAT	CAKE
HAM	SOME
PAN	TON
PIG	AGE

Make a wish!

Barbie is wishing on this magic star...
Draw what you imagine she has wished for.

Barbie Magazine

Packed with:

Fab stories
Puzzles
Games
Fashion
Make-its
Posters

Fashion & Friends

Barbie ™

Issue No. 68

FREE Hair Bobbles!

Not suitable for children under 36 months due to small parts. Supplied by HMA Ltd. Bucks HP19 8DZ. Please retain this information for future reference.

If your Free Gift is missing from here, please tell your newsagent.

Meet Spot Scene Barbie Inside!

Fantastic free gift with *every* issue!

On sale every 3 weeks at supermarkets and all good newsagents!

Barbie ™

52

For information on subscriptions, call our Credit Card Hotline on 01795 414902.

Colour Barbie using magical colours!

Match these butterflies into pairs and colour the pair you like best.

Can you spot five differences between these two pictures?

Use the picture clues to fill in the
grid and reveal a magic phrase!

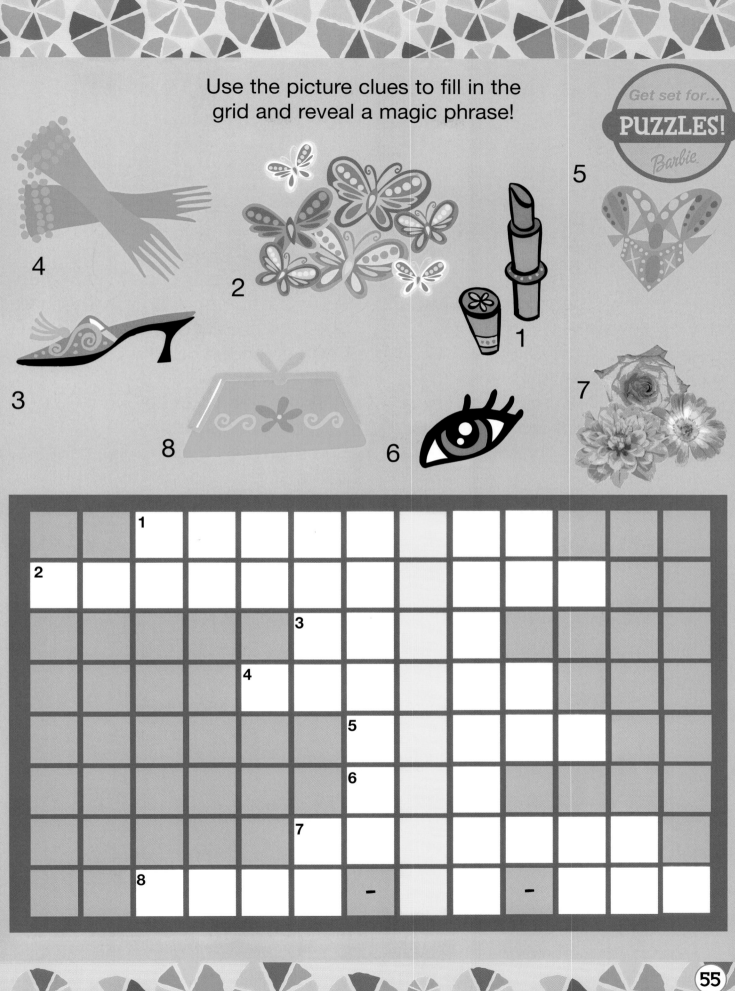

The Friendship Bracelet

**"My bedroom is a special place
where I spend time with my friends."**

It was nearly Christmas and we were having a bedroom party – strictly girls-only! Christie and Teresa were laying out the equipment – eye shadow, blusher, lip gloss and brushes! I was lining up the nail varnishes. Kira was sorting out my jumbled collection of scrunchies, hair bands and pins. We were going to have fun!

"Where's designer babe?" asked Kira, making a start on Teresa's hair. "She'll be here soon," I promised. "Don't call her that! She can't help it if she's always better dressed than the rest of us! I wonder what she'll be wearing today?" "She promised to bring her new diamante jeans for me to try on," said Kira. Just then, she appeared.

Get set to...
READ!
Barbie.

"Josie! We were just talking about you..."

We all stopped what we were doing and looked.
Josie was oddly dressed in an old tracksuit, she
had no make-up on and wasn't carrying her usual
collection of shopping bags.
"Have you brought your new jeans?" asked Kira.
"And that gorgeous party dress you bought last
week?"
"No. I took it back – OK?" snapped
Josie, taking us all by surprise. "Is that a
problem?"
No-one knew what to say.
"Yes, obviously it is," she continued. "So I might
as well go. I'm not staying where I'm not wanted."
And out she walked.

We were stunned into silence.
"What was that all about?" said Teresa.
"Did I say something wrong?" asked Kira.
"Fine way to speak to your friends!"
added Christie.
None of us were in a party mood any more.
"Let's pack away," I suggested. "We'll do it again
some other time."

I didn't sleep well that night. On Monday morning I really wanted to speak to Josie, but she wasn't at school. Mrs Gavan said she had called in sick.

"She obviously can't be bothered with us anymore," said Teresa, "or she would have phoned to apologise."

"Yes. Storming out like that! There was no need for it," agreed Kira. "Maybe she's found some new friends... with more designer labels than us!"

"We don't need her anyway," sniffed Christie.

"Don't be like that," I said. "I've known Josie all my life. We were at nursery together! I'm sure there's something wrong. I'm going to find out..."

I went to her house after school. It was one of the grandest houses in town. But there was no sign of life at the windows, and, in the front garden a sign which said 'SOLD'.

"How could she leave without saying goodbye?" said Kira the following day. "It just doesn't add up. She hasn't even told us where she's moved to."

"Hey, you've given me an idea," I said. "My Mum has a friend who works in the estate agent's. Maybe I can find out."

Later that day, after a quick phone call, I had my answer. "Claverton House?" I repeated, when my Mum told me. "But that's a block of flats! Surely Josie's family haven't moved there?"

"Flat 39," said my Mum. "Why don't you go round?"

I ran to my room. My allowance hadn't stretched to buying Christmas presents, so I'd made each of my friends a friendship bracelet. I chose the prettiest one and wrapped it up. Josie was my oldest friend, and nothing was going to change that.

I found Flat 39 on the third floor and rang the bell. Josie answered looking pale and tired. I could see the pile of removal boxes stacked up behind her. Her brother and sister were fighting. "You found us then," she said, quietly.

"I wanted you to have this..." I said, handing her the gift.

She took it and went paler than ever. "Thanks. I don't have anything to give you back. Sorry, Barbie. It's better if you leave now. Goodbye."

I didn't tell the others what had happened. It made me feel sad when I thought about it. Christmas wasn't going to be the same this year.
The last day of term soon came and everyone gathered around the tree outside school for carols. It was a beautiful evening, cold and crisp, just as it should be. I held my song sheet in gloved hands, arm in arm with Christie and Teresa. We had just started on the last verse of 'Hark the Herald Angels', when I saw a familiar face in the crowd. It was Josie. She smiled and pushed her way through to stand next to me.

We sang loudly together and when the carol was finished she pulled me to one side.
"Thanks for this..." she said, pulling up the sleeve of her coat to reveal the friendship bracelet I had made.
"It's lovely to see you," I said, suddenly feeling warm inside.
"I couldn't hide for ever," she replied. "My dad's business is in trouble. That's why we had to move. I hope it won't be for long. I felt so bad when I came to your bedroom party and everyone asked me where all my designer clothes were. I thought it was all you liked me for."

"Oh, how could you think that?" I said.

"I know... it was silly. But I felt so bad. Then, when you gave me this, I realised that friendship isn't about what you have…" Her voice trailed off.

"It's about giving and sharing," I said. "Just like Christmas!"

She smiled and gave me a hug. And, as we looked over at the tree and the lights reflected in the faces of our friends, she added,

"It's true what they say. The best things in life really are free."

It's Christmas! Barbie has been busy at the shops!
Can you match the items to their shadows?

Can you find ten handbags hidden in this picture?

Colour Barbie so that she looks her
very best for Christmas!

THE ANSWERS!

PAGE 15

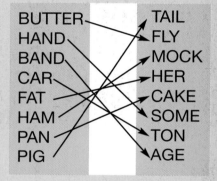

Badminton

Cricket

Baseball

Tennis

Golf

Ice Hockey

Basketball

Football

20.18.25.   25.15.21.18.   2.5.19.20

TRY YOUR BEST

PAGE 48

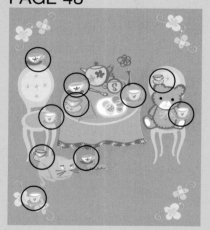

PAGE 54

PAGE 27

HBSRU
BRUSH

REAPP
PAPER

LEASE
EASEL

TRAWE
WATER

LINCEP
PENCIL

NAPTI
PAINT

PAGE 49

```
T E A P O T T C A R X N A
E O K N S P O O N C N R T
A G N C C A K O P L A T E
C Y I T B C A K E S P R I
U F F H E Y S I N V K E N
P H E S A U C E R A I F R
B E T C S S U G A R N E T
```

Route C to Barbie's tea party!

PAGE 55

```
    L I P S T I C K
  B U T T E R F L I E S
        S H O E
      G L O V E S
        H E A R T
        E Y E
      F L O W E R S
  M A K E - U P - B A G
```

PAGE 28

RUBY - RED
SNOW - WHITE
FOREST - GREEN
SKY - BLUE
BABY - PINK
TANGERINE - ORANGE
SUNSHINE - YELLOW
MIDNIGHT -BLACK

PAGE 50

BUTTER — TAIL
HAND — FLY
BAND — MOCK
CAR — HER
FAT — CAKE
HAM — SOME
PAN — TON
PIG — AGE

PAGE 62

GOODBYE!

"Bye for now, girls.
I hope you have
enjoyed your annual.

It's been fun! See you
again next year!"